THIS DOG
LOVES YOU TOO MUCH

For my little brother, the biggest dog nut I know.
And for Meg, whom we miss – LA

For Toby, my favourite dog. I wonder if I type the word
'Biscuit' you will go as crazy as when I say it? – KA

STRIPES PUBLISHING
An imprint of the Little Tiger Group
1 Coda Studios, 189 Munster Road,
London SW6 6AW

First published in Great Britain in 2018

Text copyright © Lauren Ace, 2018
Illustrations copyright © Katie Abey, 2018

ISBN: 978-1-84715-908-3

The right of Lauren Ace and Katie Abey to be identified as the
author and illustrator of this work respectively has been asserted by them
in accordance with the Copyright, Designs and Patents Act, 1988.

Printed and bound in China.
STP/1800/0159/0817
10 9 8 7 6 5 4 3 2 1

THIS DOG
LOVES YOU TOO MUCH

LAUREN ACE & KATIE ABEY

Hello.

My human is my best friend.

He's the greatest human in the world. I love him SO much.

This is what I would tell him if I could speak Human.

I can totally fit here.
Don't you move a muscle.
I just want to be close to you.

I can't believe you left this here for me.
It's not even my birthday.
You're the best.

I really want you to throw the stick,
but I don't want to let go of the stick.
Any suggestions?

This porcelain water bowl is
so fancy. You spoil me.

Are all of these for me? I must have been a really good boy this year.

I can help with that.
I am a domestic god.

Careful. I don't like the way that giant dog is looking at us.

I've taken up landscape gardening.
You can fire that strange woman
with the shovel.

I'm ready! Where are we going?

I would do anything for you but this
is really testing the limits of my love.

You missed a bit. Mmm ... coconut.

I know how much you hate being parted from me, so now you never have to leave the house again.

I just love the feeling of the wind
in my ears when I'm road trippin'
with my best bud.

You mentioned the B-word this morning, so I thought I'd save you the trouble.

Like it?
I call it Eau de Fox Poo.

You're home! You're home!
I love you! Never leave me again!

Come on in, the water is lovely,
and you really need to work
on your doggy paddle.

Did you say "WALKIES"?
I was born ready. Let's do this.

This is the one. I've been searching
for the biggest and best stick,
just for you.

You must really love me.

It's me! Obviously it's me.
I am the best boy of them all.
It is me, right?

I'm sorry, I'm sorry, I'm sorry –
it wasn't me, it was my tail...

I have no idea why you've thrown away all this perfectly good food but I'm happy to save you the trouble of taking out the bins.

I don't know what I did …
but all I can say is, I'm sorry.

Well, they do say imitation is the
sincerest form of flattery.

Please come away from the window.
I think the world might be ending.

Just keeping it warm for you.

If you won't let me sleep in your bed
with you, this is the next best thing.

Hello! Don't forget your best friend,
will you?

I can't take the credit this time.
She knows that was you.

Wait a minute, nothing good has
ever happened in this place.
Please take me home.

No rush but I need a wee, and I'm hungry, and I've missed you while you were sleeping!

You can do it!

It was so nice of your friends to visit us. I hope they enjoy my thoughtfully chosen gifts.

Don't laugh. One of these days
I'll catch it.

Is this really necessary? I have a
perfectly good fur coat of my own,
you shouldn't have wasted
your money.

Yes, I am great with kids and I do
have the patience of a saint,
thank you for noticing.

You didn't hear what that Shih Tzu said about you. I'm just defending your honour.

Sorry. My excitement got the better of me.

I'm gonna make you proud,
I'm gonna make you proud,
I'm gonna make y— Ooh, a ball!

Why do they make these things so difficult to open? I'm just trying to save you the trouble of remembering to feed me.

He's back. Why does this guy never get the message? What does he want from us?

You're my best friend, the greatest human in the world and my devotion to you is unending.

Why won't you dance with me?
C'mon, shake it!

You keep saying we need to redecorate.
How about this?

I'll get it! I need to do my security checks before you let anyone in.
No harm will come to you on my watch.

No more #dogsofinstagram for you.
I'm right here and I'm all you need.

Today is the day. Let me catch it, just this once.

There's something very suspicious
about the Dalmatian at number 4.
I'm going to stay here and
keep an eye on him.

I don't know what she means.
Your feet smell divine to me.

I'm not moving from here until you
come home. I'll lie here all day
if I have to.

LET ME LOVE YOU.

You're not leaving me here, are you?
That thing with the birthday cake
was just a misunderstanding.

I only want what's best for you
and this guy is definitely not
to be trusted.

This is MUCH more exciting than watching humans kick a ball around. I'm glad you've seen sense.

Don't mind me, I'm just listing all
the ways you are better than
this guy's human.

Where have you been? You've been
seeing other dogs, haven't you?

I could stay like this forever.
Let's never let go.